Plants in Our World

CONTENTS

What Is a Plant?

Plant Cell

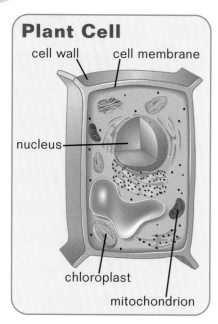

cell wall   cell membrane

nucleus

chloroplast

mitochondrion

▲ **Figure 1** The different parts of a plant cell provide protection and support for the cell; help it make, store, and use food; and perform other life functions.

READ TO UNDERSTAND

- What are some of the main characteristics of plants?
- Why are plants called producers?

VOCABULARY

species	cell wall
genus	chloroplast
kingdom	producer
division	consumer
plant	

Many ancient cultures had basic systems to categorize, or classify, living things. In our modern classification system, a group of similar organisms that can reproduce among themselves is called a **species.** A **genus** is a group of closely related species. Genus and species are the lowest, or most specific, levels of organization. The highest, or most general, level of organization is called a **kingdom.** For plants, the level below a kingdom is called a **division.** Figures 28 and 29 on page 23 give more information about the classification of living things. In this book, we will explore the wide variety of plants in the plant kingdom.

What defines a member of the plant kingdom? **Plants** are multicellular, or many-celled, organisms that can produce their own food using sunlight, air, and water. Plants do not have nervous systems, and they do not move from place to place.

Plant cells have two main structures that distinguish them from animal cells. You may know that all cells are surrounded by a cell membrane. It keeps the parts of the cell inside and lets nutrients in and wastes out. But plant cells are also surrounded by a structure called a **cell wall** (Figure 1). The cell wall is stiff, and it supports the cell. Together, all the cell walls in a plant give the plant its shape. Also present in some plant cells, but absent in animal cells, are chloroplasts. **Chloroplasts** are the structures in plant cells where food is produced using the energy from sunlight.

Every living thing needs energy to live and grow. Energy is stored in food. Since plants can make their own food, they are known as **producers.** Plants do not depend on other organisms to survive. Animals and fungi, however, are known as **consumers.** They cannot make their own food. They get energy by eating plants (Figure 2) or other animals. If all of the plants on Earth disappeared, most animals and fungi would soon die out.

▶ **Figure 2** Most organisms depend on plants for food. More than 250,000 species of plants are known.

How Do Plants Grow, Survive, and Reproduce?

Making Food and Getting Energy

Plants have one process to create food molecules that store energy. This process is called photosynthesis. Plants have a second process to break down food molecules in order to release energy. This process is called respiration.

Photosynthesis The process plants use to make food is called **photosynthesis.** *Photo* comes from the Greek word meaning "light," and *synthesis* comes from the Greek word meaning "to put together." The chemical reactions involved in photosynthesis require energy. That energy comes from sunlight. This is the "photo" part of photosynthesis. Inside the chloroplasts of a plant's cells, the chemical **chlorophyll** captures the energy from sunlight. Then the chloroplasts use that energy to chemically combine carbon dioxide (CO_2) and water (H_2O) to form the simple sugar glucose ($C_6H_{12}O_6$) and oxygen (O_2). This is the "synthesis" part of photosynthesis. Glucose is an energy-rich carbohydrate that serves as a food source for the plant. Glucose molecules are stored mostly in the plant's roots as starch. The oxygen that is produced during photosynthesis is given off through openings in the plant's leaves. Figure 3 shows the chemical equation for photosynthesis.

READ TO UNDERSTAND

- Through which two processes do plants make and use food?
- What is the main difference between vascular and nonvascular plants?
- How do responses such as dormancy and tropisms help plants survive?
- What are the two main stages of a typical plant life cycle?

VOCABULARY

photosynthesis	sperm
chlorophyll	fertilization
pigment	zygote
accessory pigment	embryo
respiration	offspring
vascular plant	chromosome
nonvascular plant	diploid
transpiration	haploid
dormancy	asexual reproduction
tropism	spore
phototropism	regeneration
gravitropism	runner
thigmotropism	rhizome
sexual reproduction	grafting
gamete	layering
egg	sporophyte
	gametophyte

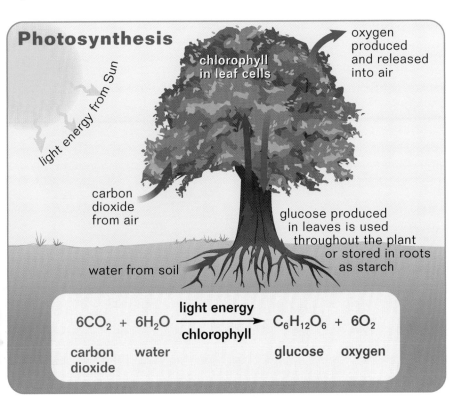

Photosynthesis

light energy from Sun

chlorophyll in leaf cells

oxygen produced and released into air

carbon dioxide from air

glucose produced in leaves is used throughout the plant or stored in roots as starch

water from soil

$$6CO_2 + 6H_2O \xrightarrow[\text{chlorophyll}]{\text{light energy}} C_6H_{12}O_6 + 6O_2$$

carbon dioxide   water   glucose   oxygen

◀ **Figure 3** During photosynthesis, a plant uses light energy from the Sun to change carbon dioxide and water into glucose and oxygen.

▲ **Figure 4** The yellow and orange colors of the carotenoids in plant leaves are usually hidden by green chlorophyll. They become visible in autumn when chlorophyll production slows down.

Chlorophyll is a **pigment,** or coloring, that gives the leaves and stems of most plants their green color. As you may know, sunlight is made up of light of every color. Since chlorophyll absorbs other colors of light, but reflects green light, it is a green pigment.

Although chlorophyll does not absorb green light, the energy of green light is not lost. **Accessory pigments** are plant pigments other than chlorophyll that also take in energy from sunlight. This energy is then passed from the accessory pigments to the chlorophyll. The carotenoids are one important group of accessory pigments (Figure 4). Carotenoids are yellow and orange, which means they reflect those colors of light and absorb the rest, including green light.

Respiration During photosynthesis, plants make and store carbohydrates such as glucose. Plants must then break down glucose in order to release and use the energy it contains. This happens in a process called respiration, which takes place in cell parts called mitochondria. Respiration is not unique to plant cells. Most living things meet their energy needs through respiration.

Many people use the word *respiration* to mean "breathing." When we breathe air into our lungs, oxygen in that air enters our blood and is delivered to body cells. It is in cells that respiration actually takes place. **Respiration** is the cellular process that uses oxygen to break down glucose into carbon dioxide and water, which releases energy (Figure 5). Cells use this energy to perform their specific life functions.

Respiration can be thought of as the opposite of photosynthesis. During photosynthesis, carbon dioxide and water are combined to form glucose and oxygen. The opposite occurs during respiration. So if respiration "undoes" photosynthesis, what's the point? Why can't a plant just use the energy from the Sun directly without going through these two complex processes? The light energy from the Sun first must be converted to a usable form—chemical energy. The carbohydrates produced by photosynthesis are really stored chemical energy. This stored energy allows a plant to grow and stay alive even at night and on cloudy days, when not enough sunlight is available for the plant to keep making carbohydrates.

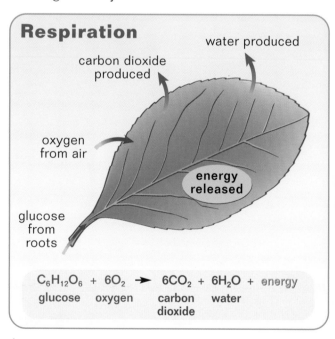

▲ **Figure 5** Respiration in plant cells releases energy from stored glucose.

Transporting Materials

Each cell in a plant carries out its own life processes. These processes include using energy to make and store food, get rid of wastes, and reproduce. So each cell must have a way to get the food, water, and dissolved minerals or nutrients needed for these processes to occur. All plants transport materials in one of two ways. In one way, materials move through tubelike structures to all parts of the plant. In the other way, materials move directly from cell to cell.

In a **vascular plant,** tiny tubelike structures carry food, water, and nutrients to all of the plant's cells. These tubelike structures are made up of vascular tissue. A tissue is a group of cells working together to do a particular job. Vascular tissue transports materials throughout a plant. Oak trees and dandelions are examples of vascular plants. Their vascular tissue carries water and nutrients from their roots up to their leaves, and food from their leaves down to their roots.

Some plants do not contain vascular tissue. These plants are called **nonvascular plants.** In nonvascular plants, food, water, and nutrients move directly from one cell to another. This process takes longer, which is one reason why nonvascular plants are usually small. Mosses are examples of nonvascular plants.

Transpiration No matter whether a plant is vascular or nonvascular, the process that causes water to move inside the plant is the same. Through the process of **transpiration,** water from inside the plant's leaves evaporates through tiny openings into the surrounding air (Figure 6). When this happens, water that is deeper in the leaves is drawn outward to take its place. That water is replaced by water even deeper in the plant, and so on down to the roots, which draw water out of the soil. This process keeps water moving throughout the entire plant.

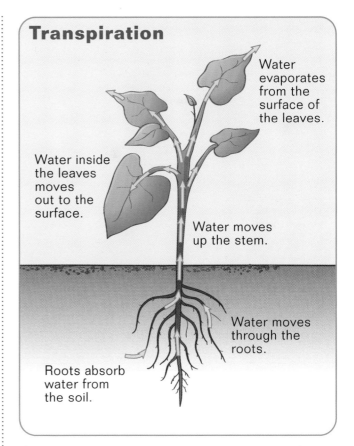

Transpiration

Water evaporates from the surface of the leaves.

Water inside the leaves moves out to the surface.

Water moves up the stem.

Water moves through the roots.

Roots absorb water from the soil.

▲ **Figure 6** During transpiration, water evaporates from a plant's leaves. New water is constantly drawn up through a plant to replace the water that evaporates.

Responding to Surroundings

All living things respond to changes in their surroundings in order to meet their needs and survive. In fact, this characteristic is part of the definition of a living thing. Plants are no exception. Plants respond to their surroundings in many ways.

Dormancy Seasonal changes in the number of hours of sunlight, air temperature, and moisture occur in most parts of the United States. When seasonal changes create poor growing conditions, many plants survive by becoming dormant. **Dormancy** is a state in which a plant's life processes slow down. Growth stops, photosynthesis stops, and the plant may appear to be dead. When conditions are once again suitable for growth, a dormant plant will return to full activity.

▲ **Figure 7** This plant shows phototropism, a response to light. Instead of growing straight up, the plant has grown toward the sunlight coming from a nearby window.

Tropisms Although plants do not move from place to place like animals, they do make movements, or **tropisms,** in response to their surroundings.

In **phototropism,** plants respond to light. For example, houseplants will grow toward the light from a nearby window (Figure 7). Sunflowers turn to follow the Sun across the sky during the course of a day. Plant roots, on the other hand, grow away from light sources.

In **gravitropism,** plants respond to gravity. Roots grow toward the pull of gravity, or "down." Stems grow away from the pull of gravity, or "up."

In **thigmotropism,** plants respond to contact. When plants such as ivy vines grow, thigmotropism allows them to remain in contact with a wall, another plant, or the ground. Climbing pea plants are another example. They have tendrils that wrap around points of contact as plants grow.

Producing Offspring

All living things reproduce, or make new living things of their own kind. Unlike most animals, plants reproduce both sexually and asexually.

Sexual Reproduction One part of a plant's life cycle involves sexual reproduction. **Sexual reproduction** is the joining of male and female sex cells, or **gametes,** to form a new individual organism. Female gametes are called **eggs,** and male gametes are called **sperm.** The pollen of flowering plants, for example, produces sperm cells. Ovules, structures usually found inside the base of a flower, produce eggs. In many plant species, a single parent plant produces both eggs and sperm. In other species, eggs and sperm are produced by separate male and female plants.

Through the process of **fertilization,** a sperm cell joins with an egg cell, forming a new cell called a **zygote.** The zygote develops into an **embryo,** an early stage in the development of a new individual organism, or **offspring.** In plants, fertilization happens in different ways, depending on the type of plant and the way it is adapted to its environment.

Each gamete (egg or sperm) from a parent plant carries information that shapes the attributes, or traits, of the offspring. This genetic information is carried in structures called **chromosomes.** Members of each species have a certain number of chromosomes in their cells. Cells that contain a species' usual number of chromosomes are called **diploid.** But in order to produce offspring with the correct number of chromosomes, gametes must contain half this number. Cells that contain half of a species' usual number of chromosomes are called **haploid.** When two haploid gametes join, their chromosomes add up to the correct number needed for a new organism.

Asexual Reproduction Another part of a plant's life cycle involves asexual reproduction. Unlike sexual reproduction, **asexual reproduction** does not require the joining of two cells. Instead, a single cell divides into two genetically identical cells.

In addition to gametes, plants produce reproductive cells called **spores.** It may surprise you to learn that all plants produce spores, from mosses and ferns to pine trees and lilies. Spores are not usually easy to see. Like a gamete, a spore is a haploid sex cell. However, unlike a gamete, which joins with another gamete in order to grow, a spore does not join with another spore in order to grow. Spores are an example of asexual reproduction. You will learn more about how gametes and spores fit into a typical plant's life cycle later in this book.

Some plants also can produce offspring asexually in other ways. For example, during **regeneration,** a piece of a plant falls off. That separate piece then grows into a new plant that is genetically identical to the parent plant.

Some plants, such as strawberries and pumpkins, reproduce asexually by growing runners (Figure 8). A **runner** is a horizontal

▲ **Figure 9** Potato plants can reproduce asexually by sprouting new leaves and roots from their tubers.

stem that branches off the main stem. Runners stretch along the top of the ground. A new plant develops at the end of each runner.

Other plants reproduce asexually using rhizomes. A **rhizome** is a horizontal stem that extends under the ground. At various points, called nodes, the rhizome sends shoots up and roots down, forming a new plant. The end of the rhizome is called a tuber, and it stores food for the new plants to use until they can produce their own. Because rhizomes and tubers store food, they are often eaten by humans and other animals. What is usually called ginger root is actually a rhizome, and a potato is a tuber (Figure 9).

Some plants grow from structures called bulbs or corms, both of which are types of short, thick stems surrounded by modified leaves. These structures allow the same plant to grow over and over again. Both bulbs and corms remain underground and send up shoots that grow into plants. If the plant is harvested or dies during the winter, a new plant grows from the same bulb or corm to replace it. Onion and tulip plants grow from bulbs, while crocuses grow from corms.

▲ **Figure 8** New strawberry plants are growing from the parent plant's runners.

So far you have read about ways that plants reproduce asexually in nature. People also have developed gardening methods that rely on asexual reproduction. One of these methods is called grafting. **Grafting** is attaching part of one plant to another plant so that the two grow together. Imagine a plant with thick, healthy roots, but weak branches. Now picture another plant with strong branches, but small roots. In grafting, a gardener cuts a branch off the second plant, then slits the stem of the first plant and inserts one end of the branch into the slit. The two pieces grow together, forming a plant with thick, healthy roots and strong branches.

Another gardening method is called layering. **Layering** involves scraping a bit of bark away from a stem or branch. Then the branch is bent over and covered with soil. The tip of the branch is left uncovered. New roots and shoots grow from the buried part of the branch, forming new plants (Figure 10). When the new plants are big enough, the gardener separates them from the parent plant.

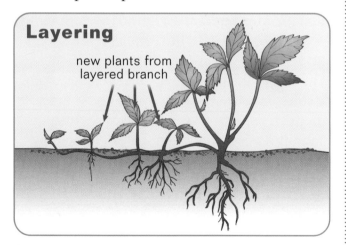

Layering
new plants from layered branch

▲ **Figure 10** Gardeners can produce many plants from an existing plant by layering.

Life Cycles As you have read, a typical plant's life cycle is complex. It involves two stages: the **sporophyte** stage and the **gametophyte** stage (Figure 11). A plant reproduces during both stages.

For most plants, the sporophyte is the familiar structure we recognize as the garden plant, tree, or shrub. The sporophyte produces spores, each of which develops into a gametophyte plant structure. Since spores are haploid and do not join together in order to produce a gametophyte, all of the cells of the gametophyte are also haploid.

In many plants, the gametophyte is small and grows on the sporophyte. For example, the flowers of a lily sporophyte produce spores that develop into other structures within the flower called pollen and ovules. The pollen and ovules are the gametophytes. In other plants, the gametophyte grows separately from the sporophyte that produced it. For example, fern sporophytes produce spores that fall to the ground and develop into separate, tiny gametophytes.

No matter what form it takes, the gametophyte plant structure produces haploid gametes (eggs and sperm). Through the process of fertilization, the egg and sperm join, resulting in a diploid zygote. In some plants, such as lilies, the zygote develops into an embryo inside a seed and grows into a new sporophyte. In other plants, such as ferns, the zygote grows more directly into a new sporophyte. Then the life cycle begins again.

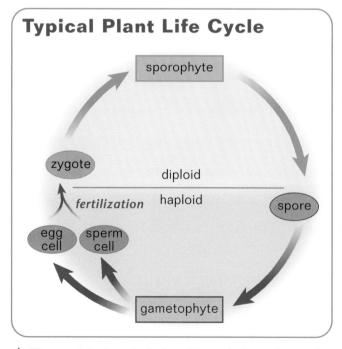

Typical Plant Life Cycle

sporophyte

zygote

diploid

fertilization haploid

spore

egg cell

sperm cell

gametophyte

▲ **Figure 11** A typical plant life cycle is made up of two stages: sporophyte and gametophyte.

Nonvascular Plants

moss

liverwort

hornwort

Characteristics

Nonvascular plants do not have vascular tissue. Within these plants, food, water, and nutrients must move directly from one cell to another. Nonvascular plants are always small. Most of their structures are only a few cells thick. A typical nonvascular plant has chloroplasts in all of its cells, so photosynthesis occurs throughout the plant.

Nonvascular plants lack true leaves, true stems, and true roots. They hold themselves onto the ground with a thin, rootlike structure called a **rhizoid.** The word *rhizoid* means "rhizome-like," but the rhizoid just holds the plant in place. It does not store any food or water for the plant as a rhizome does. If the environment dries up, the plant becomes dormant and remains that way until water returns.

The most obvious, or dominant, stage of a nonvascular plant's life is the gametophyte stage. This is unusual. For most other plants, the opposite is true—the dominant stage is the sporophyte stage. The three different types of nonvascular plants are mosses, liverworts, and hornworts (Figure 12).

Types

Mosses Just about any place on Earth can support at least one of the more than 10,000 different kinds of mosses. Peat moss, or sphagnum, is a common type of moss. Most mosses are small and low to the ground. However, a small number of mosses have cells that function similarly to vascular tissue. These mosses can grow to be 80 centimeters (about 31 inches) tall.

▲ **Figure 12** Mosses, liverworts, and hornworts are the three types of nonvascular plants. These plants have the simplest, or most primitive, structure of all plants. Today, nonvascular plants make up more than 6% of the plant species on Earth.

READ TO UNDERSTAND

- What is the dominant stage of a nonvascular plant's life?
- What are the three main types of nonvascular plants?

VOCABULARY

rhizoid

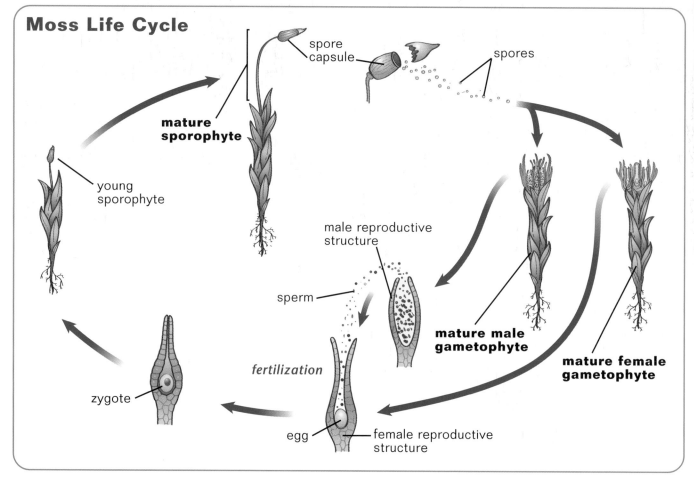

Moss Life Cycle

spore capsule

spores

mature sporophyte

young sporophyte

male reproductive structure

sperm

mature male gametophyte

mature female gametophyte

fertilization

zygote

egg

female reproductive structure

▲ **Figure 13** A moss is a nonvascular plant. In the life cycle of a nonvascular plant, what is produced by the mature sporophyte?

Liverworts The differences between liverworts and mosses can be seen only on close examination. For example, the rhizoid of a moss is made up of several cells, while the rhizoid of a liverwort is just one long cell. All liverworts fall into one of two groups. Some are long and flat, while others have structures that look like tiny leaves on stems.

Hornworts Hornworts are similar to liverworts. Hornworts get their name from their sporophytes, which have a long, thick, horn-like shape. A typical plant cell contains many chloroplasts, but each cell of a hornwort has only one chloroplast.

Reproduction

The sporophyte of a nonvascular plant produces spores (Figure 13). The spores develop into structures that spread out through the surface of the soil. Gametophytes grow from these structures. Reproductive structures on the mature gametophytes produce eggs and sperm. In order to reproduce, a nonvascular plant must be moist, because the sperm must swim through water to reach the eggs.

A fertilized egg, or zygote, grows into a sporophyte. The sporophyte is often a structure made up of a long stalk with a spore capsule attached. This structure grows from the gametophyte. In some nonvascular plants, the sporophyte does not contain any chlorophyll. It is completely dependent on the gametophyte for food. The mature sporophyte produces spores. The spore capsule eventually bursts or dries up and breaks apart, releasing the spores. When the spores are released, the life cycle begins again. Most nonvascular plants reproduce in this way.

Vascular Plants

About 94% of the plant species on Earth today are vascular plants. Vascular plants can grow taller than nonvascular plants because of their more complex transport systems. Vascular plants transport food, water, and nutrients through two types of vascular tissue: xylem and phloem. **Xylem** transports water and nutrients to all parts of the plant. It also provides structure and support. **Phloem** transports food to all parts of the plant. Xylem and phloem make up tubelike structures that are often packed together in bunches called **vascular bundles.**

Unlike a nonvascular plant, the most obvious, or dominant, stage of a vascular plant's life is the sporophyte stage. Most vascular plants have true roots, stems, and leaves. Vascular plants can be divided into two groups, according to whether or not their life cycle involves seeds.

Seedless Vascular Plants

whisk fern

true fern

club moss

horsetail

◄ **Figure 14**
Whisk ferns, true ferns, club mosses, and horsetails are the four types of seedless vascular plants. These plants have more complex structures than nonvascular plants do. Today, seedless vascular plants make up about 5% of the plant species on Earth.

Characteristics

In this section, we will explore the vascular plants that do not produce seeds. Four types of seedless vascular plants exist: whisk ferns, true ferns, club mosses, and horsetails. Despite their names, whisk ferns are not really ferns, and club mosses are not really mosses. Most seedless vascular plants have true roots, stems, and leaves. The one exception to this is the whisk fern.

Types

Whisk Ferns Whisk ferns are the simplest of all seedless vascular plants. Although whisk ferns have true stems, they do not have true roots or leaves. Instead, a whisk fern is held to the ground by a rhizome, and photosynthesis takes place in its aboveground stem.

Whisk fern gametophytes are only about 2 millimeters (about 0.08 inch) long. They do not have chloroplasts. They live under the soil and absorb nutrients directly from it. Often a fungus

READ TO UNDERSTAND

- What is the dominant stage of a vascular plant's life?
- What are the four types of seedless vascular plants?

VOCABULARY

xylem	vascular bundle
phloem	frond

that breaks down organic matter in the soil will grow through the soil and into the body of the whisk fern gametophyte. When this happens, the fungus provides the nourishment the gametophyte needs.

True Ferns True ferns grow from underground rhizomes that have roots. In various places along each rhizome, clusters of leaves grow up and into the air. These leaves are called **fronds.** Most fronds grow from 0.5 meter (about 1.6 feet) to 1 meter (about 3.3 feet) long, but some can be as large as 3.6 meters (about 12 feet). Photosynthesis occurs in a true fern's fronds, as it does in any leaf. If the environment grows cold or dries out, the fronds will die, but the rest of the fern will stay alive underground.

Club Mosses Club mosses grow close to the ground. They get their name from their tiny, club-shaped, spore-forming structures. A club moss plant also has many tiny leaves that grow in a spiral pattern around the stem, which makes the plant look like a small pine tree. As with whisk ferns, a club moss gametophyte has no chlorophyll and often receives nourishment from a soil fungus.

Horsetails The most notable feature of a horsetail sporophyte is its long, hollow stem. The stem is covered with small scaly leaves, but most photosynthesis occurs in the stem itself. Most horsetails grow less than 1 meter (about 3.3 feet) tall, but some can reach 3 meters (about 9.8 feet). At the tip of the stem is a structure that looks somewhat like a pine cone. This is where the spores are produced.

Like true ferns, horsetails grow from an underground rhizome, and the rhizome has roots growing from it. The stem of a horsetail contains silica, a material used to make glass. The silica makes the stem tough and scratchy. Horsetail stems were once used for scrubbing pots and pans before more modern cleaning products were invented.

Reproduction

When a seedless vascular plant is ready to reproduce, spores form on the underside of the sporophyte's fronds (Figure 15), on its leaves, or as knobs on the stems. The spores grow into gametophytes.

When the gametophyte develops, it is usually a very small plant that lives completely separate from the sporophyte. Most gametophytes last only long enough to produce eggs and sperm. The gametophytes of seedless vascular plants are actually nonvascular. Because of this, seedless vascular plants must live in wet or damp areas in order to thrive. The gametophytes have male sex organs that produce sperm and female sex organs that produce eggs. The eggs stay where they are, and the sperm swim through the water to them.

▲ **Figure 15** The yellow dots on the underside of the fern fronds are clusters of spores.

Seed Plants

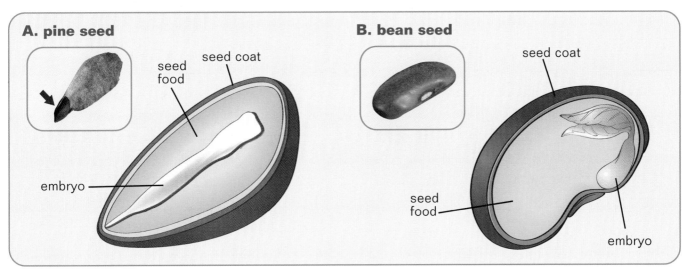

A. pine seed

seed food

seed coat

embryo

B. bean seed

seed coat

seed food

embryo

▲ **Figure 16** All seeds contain a plant embryo and food for the embryo.

Characteristics

In this section, we will explore the seed-producing vascular plants. In addition to seeds and vascular tissue, all seed plants have true leaves, stems, and roots. About 89% of the plant species on Earth today are seed-producing plants.

Seeds A **seed** is a plant structure that contains and protects a plant embryo, or tiny sporophyte (Figure 16). Seeds can form on the outside of leaves, in tough and woody structures called **cones,** or from flowers. Seeds contain not only the embryo, but also food for the embryo to use as it grows. The embryo needs a food source until it becomes a seedling and can make its own food by photosynthesis.

All seeds are protected by a layer called the **seed coat.** For example, the hull surrounding an unpopped kernel of popcorn is a seed coat. The shell of a coconut is a part of its seed coat. You might think the seed coat of the peanut is its shell, but it is actually the red, papery layer around each nut inside.

The embryo inside a seed is alive, but dormant. In this state, the embryo can survive for long periods of time in cold, dry conditions that would kill an adult plant. When the proper conditions occur, the embryo emerges from dormancy and starts to grow. This early development of the embryo is called **germination.** When a seed germinates, its seed coat splits. This allows a root to begin growing down into the soil. Once the root grows enough to anchor the germinating plant, a shoot grows up from the seed. Over time, the shoot develops a stem and leaves.

READ TO UNDERSTAND

• What is the function of a seed?

• Where do the seeds form in a gymnosperm? How about in an angiosperm?

• What are some ways to tell monocots and dicots apart?

VOCABULARY

seed	ovule
cone	pollination
seed coat	angiosperm
germination	flower
leaf	ovary
pith	fruit
cambium	cotyledon
cork cambium	monocot
cork	dicot
bark	sepal
root	petal
gymnosperm	stamen
pollen	pistil

Inside a Leaf

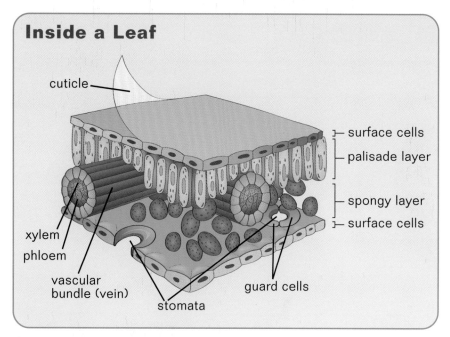

cuticle

surface cells

palisade layer

spongy layer

surface cells

xylem

phloem

vascular
bundle (vein)

guard cells

stomata

▲ **Figure 17** Leaves are made up of several distinct layers. The parts of a leaf assist in photosynthesis, respiration, and transpiration.

Leaves In most plants, photosynthesis, respiration, and transpiration all take place primarily in the leaves. A **leaf** is a plant organ made up of many different layers of tissue (Figure 17). The outer layer is made up of surface cells. A waxy film called the cuticle covers the surface cells and keeps in moisture. Openings called stomata are located on the underside of a leaf. Guard cells open and close the stomata so carbon dioxide, water vapor, and other gases can go in and out of the leaf.

Inside a leaf are two more layers, called the palisade layer and the spongy layer. The palisade layer contains many chloroplasts. The spongy layer includes the vascular bundles, also called leaf veins. The spongy layer also serves as a storage place for carbon dioxide and water vapor.

Stems A stem has two main functions. First, a stem gives a plant structure and supports the plant's leaves. Second, a stem contains vascular tissue that carries food, water, and minerals between the roots and the leaves. In addition, green stems can perform photosynthesis. Stems also can serve as a storage place for food or water in a plant.

The stems of nearly all plants grow taller. Some plants, such as trees, have stems that grow thicker, too. Although most stems grow vertically, some creep along the ground horizontally or climb and twist around a supporting plant or structure. A very young stem with leaves on it is called a shoot. Branches are older stems with shoots or other branches growing from them.

Stems can be classified as either herbaceous or woody. Herbaceous stems are green and grow taller, but not much thicker over time. Herbaceous stems usually last for only one growing season. Woody stems are sturdier, are longer lasting, and grow both taller and thicker over time. Plants that produce woody stems are known as trees or shrubs. The main stem of a woody plant is called a trunk.

Inside a Tree

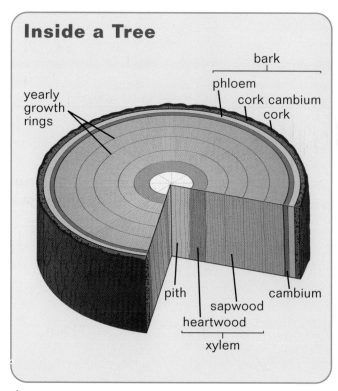

bark

phloem

cork cambium

cork

yearly
growth
rings

pith

cambium

sapwood

heartwood

xylem

▲ **Figure 18** Wood is made up of many layers, each with its own function.

Figure 18 shows a cross section of a tree's woody stem. The center, or core, of the wood is made up of spongy food storage cells called **pith.** Outside the pith is a layer of inactive xylem tissue called heartwood. The heartwood is surrounded by active xylem tissue called sapwood. Outside the sapwood is a very thin layer of tissue called **cambium.** Cambium is only one or two cells thick. Outside the cambium is a layer of phloem tissue.

The main function of cambium cells is to reproduce, causing the trunk to grow thicker. The inside layer of cambium produces new xylem cells. The outside layer of the cambium produces new phloem cells. The cambium is most active between spring and fall each year and slows down in winter. This yearly cycle of activity results in the xylem growth rings that can be seen in a tree trunk. As the inside layer of the cambium produces more xylem cells, the xylem core thickens. Eventually, the cells toward the center of the core die and harden, becoming heartwood.

Outside the phloem is another layer called the **cork cambium.** On the outside, it produces a layer of protective cells called **cork.** Together, the phloem, cork cambium, and cork make up the layer we call **bark.** Cork cells are made of a waxy substance, so they help keep moisture in the wood. Cork also protects woody stems from being eaten by insects and other animals. As soon as cork cells mature, they die. Since dead cork cells do not provide much nutrition, most insects do not eat them.

Roots Roots have two main functions. First, roots absorb water and dissolved minerals or nutrients from the soil. Then the xylem transports these materials throughout the plant. Second, roots anchor a plant and give it support. Most plants have roots that hold the plant to the ground. However, some plants, such as orchids, have roots that anchor the plant to whatever surface it grows on, such as a rock, a wall, or another plant. This means the roots are in the open air.

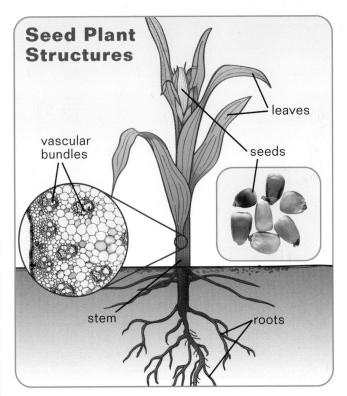

Seed Plant Structures

▲ **Figure 19** The five main structures shown on this corn plant work together to help the plant meet its needs for energy, growth, survival, and reproduction.

To review, all seed-producing plants have seeds, vascular tissue, and true leaves, stems, and roots (Figure 19). However, there are differences among seed plants that allow us to classify them into two groups: gymnosperms and angiosperms.

Gymnosperms

A **gymnosperm** is a plant whose seeds form on the outside of a leaf or other structure. This means that the seeds are exposed to the air. The word *gymnosperm* comes from two Greek words meaning "naked seed." Gymnosperms make up less than 1% of all species of seed plants.

Most gymnosperms are either trees or shrubs. However, a few species look like vines. Most gymnosperms are evergreens, which means that they keep their green color all year long. They have long, sharp, needle-shaped leaves. A gymnosperm's seeds are usually carried and protected by a cone. Gymnosperms have woody stems.

cycad

ginkgo

gnetophyte

conifer

▲ **Figure 20** The four types of gymnosperms alive today are cycads, ginkgos, gnetophytes, and conifers.

Types **Cycads** are gymnosperms that look like short, squat palm trees. However, cycads are not related to palm trees at all. About 200 million years ago, around the time of the dinosaurs, cycads were very common. Today, fewer species of cycads exist and they grow mostly in tropical and subtropical regions.

Ginkgos also were common about 200 million years ago. Today, only one species of ginkgo has escaped extinction. It is the ginkgo tree, or *Ginkgo biloba*. The name *biloba* comes from the fact that the tree's leaves are divided into two lobes. The female trees produce a seed structure that looks like a nut or a fruit.

Gnetophytes are divided into three groups, each of which is quite different from the other two. *Welwitschia* (shown above) grows only two leaves its entire life. They are very long and flap around in the wind, often tearing into thinner strips. Its reproductive structures grow inside cones. *Gnetum* looks like a vine or small tree. Its reproductive structures grow inside flowerlike structures. *Ephedra* is a shrub or a woody vine. Its reproductive structures also grow inside flowerlike structures.

Conifers include such well-known trees as pines, firs, and junipers. The word *conifer* means "cone bearing," and indeed all conifers produce cones. Most conifers have very thin, needle-shaped leaves. Most are evergreens, but some, such as the larch, drop their needles every year. Some species of conifer include individuals that are the oldest and tallest living things on the planet. A bristlecone pine in California has been living for 4,600 years. Some giant redwoods are more than 100 meters (about 328 feet) tall.

Reproduction Most gymnosperms have both male and female cones on the same plant (Figure 21). Cycads and ginkgos are the exceptions. The whole plants are either male or female. Female cones are woody. Male cones are small and typically last only through the springtime. A substance called pollen usually develops from spores that form on the scales of a male cone. **Pollen** contains the male sex cells, or sperm. Ovules grow from spores on the female cones. **Ovules** contain the female sex cells, or eggs. Each scale on a female cone contains two ovules.

The process of getting the pollen to the ovules is called **pollination.** In gymnosperms, this usually occurs when pollen grains are blown through the air and land on a sticky opening near each ovule. Some kinds of pine trees produce great amounts of yellow pollen. You may have seen this powder coating roads and puddles in the springtime. Making so much pollen helps to make sure that some of it lands on the female cones.

Once pollination occurs, the pollen begins to grow a kind of tube down into the ovule. When the pollen tube enters the ovule, this signals the ovule to produce eggs. The pollen tube delivers sperm cells, which fertilize the eggs. In some species, such as fir trees, this process takes only a few weeks. In others, such as many pines, springtime pollination does not result in eggs being fertilized until the early summer of the following year.

Next, the process of seed ripening begins. As with pollination, the length of time it takes a seed to ripen varies with the species. Each mature seed contains one embryo. When the seeds are ripe, they blow off the cone and into the air. Some of the seeds land on the ground. If the conditions are right, one or more of the seeds will germinate and grow into a new tree.

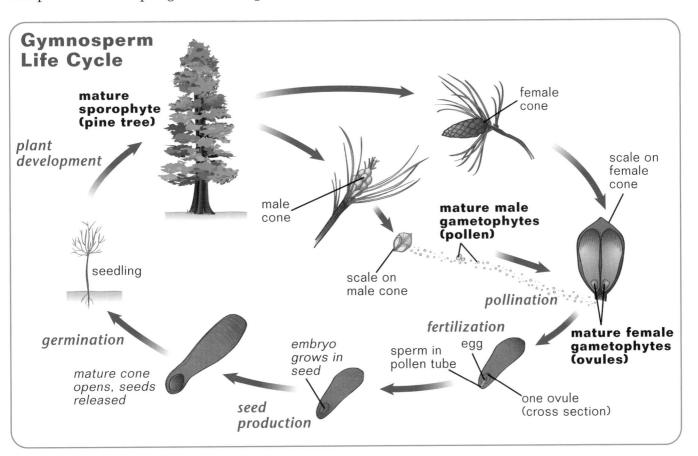

Gymnosperm Life Cycle

mature sporophyte (pine tree)

plant development

female cone

scale on female cone

male cone

mature male gametophytes (pollen)

scale on male cone

pollination

seedling

germination

fertilization

mature cone opens, seeds released

embryo grows in seed

sperm in pollen tube

egg

mature female gametophytes (ovules)

seed production

one ovule (cross section)

▲ **Figure 21** A pine tree is a type of gymnosperm called a conifer. The life cycle of a gymnosperm includes pollination, fertilization, seed production, germination, and plant development.

▲ **Figure 22** The strawberry's seeds are located in the surface of the fruit. The apricot's seed—sometimes called a pit or stone—is deep within the fruit.

Angiosperms

An **angiosperm** is a plant whose seeds are located inside a fruit. After fertilization, the ovary grows around the seeds and covers them. The word *angiosperm* comes from two Greek words that mean "covered seed." Angiosperms make up more than 99% of all species of seed plants.

Like all plants, angiosperms produce their own food through photosynthesis. But many different types of angiosperms exist, and some species have other adaptations to get nutrition as well. For example, some angiosperms supplement their diet with nourishment from decaying organic matter. Some act as parasites, obtaining nourishment from another living organism.

All angiosperms have flowers and fruit. A **flower** contains the reproductive structures of an angiosperm. For this reason, angiosperms are often called flowering plants. Inside the flower is the ovary. The **ovary** is the structure that contains the ovule, which produces the egg. As the seeds of an angiosperm develop, so does the ovary. Eventually, the ovary ripens into the fruit. The **fruit** is the developed ovary that surrounds and protects the seeds (Figure 22). Peaches, oranges, cherries, and tomatoes are familiar fruits. Nuts are also a type of fruit. So are pea pods, pumpkins, and the winged "helicopters" that spin down from a maple tree.

Types Angiosperms can be divided into two groups: monocots and dicots. All angiosperm seeds contain tiny, leaflike structures called **cotyledons.** In most seeds, it is the cotyledons that provide food for the embryo. A plant whose seeds contain only one cotyledon is called a monocotyledon, or **monocot.** A plant whose seeds contain two cotyledons is called a dicotyledon, or **dicot.** Monocots and dicots have other differences as well (Figure 23). A second difference is the way their vascular tissues are arranged. The vascular bundles of a monocot are scattered irregularly throughout the stem. In a dicot stem, the vascular bundles are arranged in a ring. Tomato plants and maple trees are examples of dicots, while corn and rice are monocots.

	Monocots	**Dicots**
cotyledons	one cotyledon	two cotyledons
vascular tissue	scattered vascular bundles	vascular bundles in a ring
leaves	parallel veins	network of veins
roots	spread-out roots	taproot
flower parts	in threes	in fours or fives

▲ **Figure 23** This chart shows the main differences between monocots and dicots.

Another way to tell monocots and dicots apart is by their leaves. Most monocot leaves have major veins that are parallel to one another. They may be connected by smaller veins, but the large, parallel ones usually stand out. The leaves of a dicot, though, usually have a branching network of veins across the leaf.

Monocots and dicots also have differences in their root systems and number of flower parts. The roots of most monocots usually spread out below the surface of the soil. In contrast, dicots often have one large vertical root, called a taproot, with smaller roots branching from it. The flower parts, such as the petals, of most monocots are found in multiples of three. Most dicots have flower parts in multiples of four or five.

Reproduction Angiosperm reproduction takes place inside the flower (Figure 24). Leafy structures called **sepals** help protect a developing flower before it opens. Once a flower opens, its **petals** help protect the other parts inside. The male part of an angiosperm flower is called a **stamen.** A stamen has two parts. The tip of the stamen, called the anther, produces the pollen, or male gametophyte. The rest of the stamen is called the filament. It holds the anther away from the female parts of the plant. This helps prevent the flower from fertilizing itself.

The female part of an angiosperm flower is called a **pistil.** A pistil has three parts. The tip of the pistil, called the stigma, collects pollen from other plants. The style connects the stigma to the ovary. The ovary produces the ovule, which is the female gametophyte that produces egg cells.

Different angiosperms have different ways of achieving pollination. Some, like oak trees, simply release pollen into the air. Other angiosperms rely on insects to help with pollination. Colorful petals help to attract insects such as honeybees. A flower produces nectar, which the bee collects and later turns into honey. The nectar is deep in the center of the flower. To get to it, the bee must crawl past the anthers. Pollen from the anthers sticks to the bee's body. The bee then flies to another flower and crawls in to collect its nectar. Some of the pollen from the first flower rubs off the bee and onto the stigma of the second flower. Stigmas are often sticky, which helps get the pollen off the bee.

Angiosperm life cycles, like those of other plants, vary in length. Annuals are plants that have a one-year life cycle. In one growing season, an annual germinates from a seed, grows, develops flowers and seeds, and then completely dies. Petunias and tomatoes are annuals.

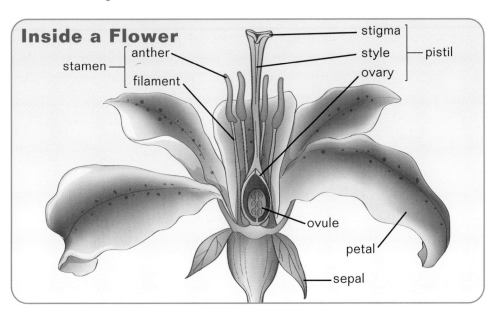

Inside a Flower

stamen
- anther
- filament

stigma
style — pistil
ovary

ovule

petal

sepal

◄ **Figure 24**
Most angiosperms, such as this lily, have both pistils (female parts) and stamens (male parts) in the same flower. But some kinds of angiosperms, such as begonias, have separate male and female flowers on the same plant. Still other angiosperms, such as holly, grow as entirely separate male or female plants.

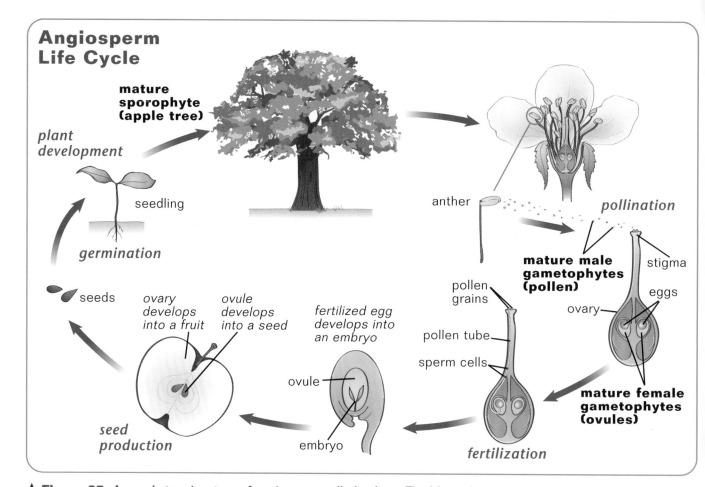

Angiosperm Life Cycle

plant development

mature sporophyte (apple tree)

seedling

germination

seeds

ovary develops into a fruit

ovule develops into a seed

fertilized egg develops into an embryo

ovule

embryo

seed production

fertilization

anther

pollination

mature male gametophytes (pollen)

stigma

pollen grains

eggs

pollen tube

ovary

sperm cells

mature female gametophytes (ovules)

▲ **Figure 25** An apple tree is a type of angiosperm called a dicot. The life cycle of an angiosperm includes pollination, fertilization, seed production, germination, and plant development. In angiosperms, what structure becomes the fruit?

Biennials are plants that have a two-year life cycle. In the first year, a biennial grows leaves and stores food in its roots. In the second year, the plant produces flowers and seeds, then dies. Parsley and foxglove are biennials.

Perennials are plants that have a life cycle longer than two years. A perennial's above-ground parts may die during the winter, but the plant will produce new leaves and flowers each year. Peonies and asparagus are herbaceous perennials. Apple trees are woody perennials.

Figure 25 shows the life cycle of an apple tree, one example of an angiosperm. The mature sporophyte produces flowers that contain spores, which develop into pollen and ovules. Pollination is generally done by insects. Once pollen is on the stigma, a pollen tube forms down through the style toward one of the ovules in the base. Sperm cells, usually two, travel through the tube to the ovule.

When they reach the ovule, one sperm cell joins with the egg to form the zygote, which develops into the embryo. But there are other cells in the ovule in addition to the egg. One of these cells joins with the second sperm cell. This grows into the tissue that will provide nutrition for the embryo inside the seed.

As the seeds develop inside the ovary, the flower dies and the petals fall off. The ovary that surrounds the seeds grows larger and develops into a fruit. Ripe fruits fall off the tree and often end up somewhere else, carried by wind, water, or animals. Eventually, the fruit decays, exposing the seeds to the environment. If the conditions are right, one or more of the seeds will germinate and develop into new plants.

Ethnobotanists: People, Plants, and Medicine

Tomatoes, corn, and chocolate are found today in supermarkets throughout the world. Originally, the plants these foods come from grew only in North and South America. The plants were first used by people who lived in the areas where they grew. Over time, the plants were brought to the rest of the world by explorers. Today, knowledge of local, or native, plants is brought to other parts of the world by ethnobotanists. An **ethnobotanist** studies the way people use native plants. The knowledge collected helps people around the world develop new medicines, clothing, and construction materials.

Much attention is now given to plants that are used to make medicines. In the early 1600s, people living in the Andes Mountains in South America taught Spanish missionaries how to make a medicine from cinchona bark to treat fevers. The active substance in cinchona bark is called quinine. Quinine-based drugs are still used today to treat malaria, a life-threatening blood infection.

People in the Caribbean island nation of Guadeloupe traditionally drank pineapple juice to aid digestion. In 1891 a chemical called bromelain was found to be the active substance in the juice. Bromelain speeds up the breakdown of proteins, including proteins in food. Proteins also occur in blood clots, which can lead to heart attacks. There is evidence that bromelain may help prevent clots.

Most ethnobotanists begin their training with a degree in biology or botany. Then they get additional training in other fields. They study anthropology, linguistics, and sociology to better communicate with people around the world who know traditional uses of plants. Studying chemistry helps ethnobotanists understand the active substances in plants.

Opportunities to find plants and learn about their uses are decreasing. Rain forests contain many plant species that have not yet been explored. However, hundreds of thousands of acres of rain forest are being destroyed every day. Also, as contact with industrial societies increases, the traditional ways of people in rain forest areas are changing. Knowledge about the uses of plants is not always passed down to new generations. So a race for knowledge is on, and the field of ethnobotany is growing.

▲ **Figure 26**
Catharanthus roseus (rosy periwinkle) is a rain forest plant used in cancer treatment. Today, many of the medicines we use contain ingredients that were first discovered in plants. Some of these medicines contain actual plant substances. Other medicines contain chemical copies of the plant substances that were developed in a laboratory.

About Seed Dispersal

Seedlings usually do not thrive if they are growing next to an adult plant. The larger plant gets all the water and space and blocks the sunlight. So most plants need to disperse their seeds, or send them away from the parent plant.

One way seeds are dispersed is by animals. Some plants, such as apple trees, have shiny or sweet-smelling fruit. Animals eat the fruit. By the time the seeds pass through the animal's digestive tract and reach the ground, the seeds are far away from the parent plant. Squirrels and other animals often gather seeds and nuts and hide them for the coming winter. In many cases, the animal never returns to its hiding place, and the seeds sprout in their new location.

Some seeds have a special shape that helps them catch a ride on animals or people. These seeds have cases covered with tiny spines or hooks that catch on fur, skin, or clothing. Common examples of these include the various kinds of burrs.

Seeds also can be dispersed by water or by wind. Some plants, such as water lilies and coconut palms, have seeds that float. The water carries them far away to a new home.

The dandelion is a plant that grows individual seeds inside tiny fruits. Tufts of light, hairlike structures grow out of the fruits. When the wind catches these structures, they are carried through the air, with the fruit dangling beneath.

Maple and spruce trees are two of the many plants whose seeds have "wings." They make the falling seed flutter or spin, which slows its fall. The longer the seed stays in the air, the farther it might be blown before it hits the ground.

Some plants, such as tumbleweeds, dry out and break away from their roots. The wind pushes the entire plant along. The plant drops and spreads seeds as it goes.

Other plants, such as impatiens, grow their seeds inside a small capsule. When the seeds are ripe, the capsule explodes, scattering the seeds over a fair distance.

The jack pine is an example of a plant whose seeds lie dormant until the parent plant dies. The seeds are held to the cone by a sticky resin. When there is a forest fire, the resin breaks down and the seeds are released. The fire kills many adult trees, but it also releases the seeds that will start a new generation.

▲ **Figure 27** Seeds can be dispersed, or moved away from the parent plant, in many different ways.